# The Gr LOVE SONGS Of The 60s

**Wise Publications**
part of The Music Sales Group
London/New York/Paris/Sydney/Copenhagen/Berlin/Madrid/Tokyo

Published by

Wise Publications
14-15 Berners Street, London W1T 3LJ, UK.

Exclusive Distributors:

Music Sales Limited
Distribution Centre, Newmarket Road,
Bury St Edmunds, Suffolk IP33 3YB, UK.

Music Sales Pty Limited
120 Rothschild Avenue, Rosebery,
NSW 2018, Australia.

Order No. AM986788
ISBN 1-84609-707-X
This book © Copyright 2006 Wise Publications,
a division of Music Sales Limited.

Front cover photo courtesy of Hulton Archive/Getty Images.
Back cover photographs courtesy of LFI.

Printed in the EU.

www.musicsales.com

Your Guarantee of Quality

As publishers, we strive to produce every book
to the highest commercial standards.

The book has been carefully designed
to minimise awkward page turns and to
make playing from it a real pleasure.

Particular care has been given to specifying
acid-free, neutral-sized paper made from pulps
which have not been elemental chlorine bleached.

This pulp is from farmed sustainable forests and
was produced with special regard for the environment.

Throughout, the printing and binding have been
planned to ensure a sturdy, attractive publication
which should give years of enjoyment.

If your copy fails to meet our high standards,
please inform us and we will gladly replace it.

# And I Love Her

Words & Music by John Lennon & Paul McCartney

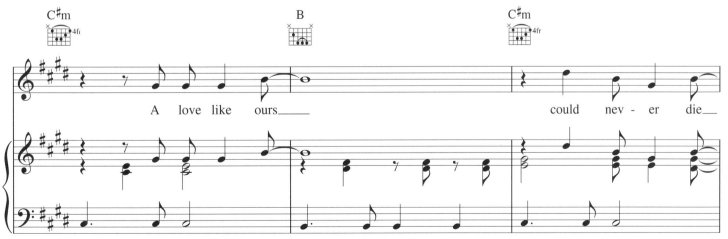

6

will nev - er die.\_\_\_\_\_ And I love\_\_ her.\_\_

\_\_ her.\_\_\_\_\_

# Anyone Who Had A Heart

Words by Hal David
Music by Burt Bacharach

take me_____ in his arms and_____ love me too. You could-n't real-ly have a heart and hurt me_____ like you hurt me and be so un-

9

so.  An - y - one who had a heart would

take  me_____  in his arms  and_____  love me

too.  You  could - n't real - ly have a heart  and

hurt me_____ like you hurt me and be so un -

1.
- true.          What am I to do?_

2.
- true._____ An-y-one who had a heart would love me
you?_____

too._____ An-y-one who had a heart would sure-ly take me__ in his arms and__ al-ways

# Baby Now That I've Found You

Words & Music by Tony Macauley & John MacLeod

need_____ me.___

Ba - by, ba - by since first_____ we met_____ I

knew in this heart of mine___ the love we had___ could

not be___ bad.___ I say right, and bide my___ time.___

16

17

# Brown Eyed Girl

Words & Music by Van Morrison

1. Hey where did we go?
2. What-ev-er hap-pened?
3. So hard to find my way

Days__ when the rains__
To Tues-day and so__
now__ that I'm all__

__ came,
__ slow,
__ on my own.

down__ in the hol-low,
go-ing__ down the old mine,
I saw you just the oth-er day,

playin' a new____ game.
with a tran-sis-tor ra - di - o.
my, how you have____ grown.
Laugh-ing and a'
Stand-ing in the
Cast my mem-'ry

run - ning, hey___ hey
sun - light laugh - ing,
back there, Lord,_____
skip-ping and a' jump-ing,
hid - ing be - hind a rain-bow's wall,
some-times I'm o - ver-come think-in' 'bout it,

in the mis-ty morn - ing fog____ with our
slip-ping and a' slid - ing all a - long
laugh-ing and a' run - ning, hey,___ hey, be -

21

# Can't Help Falling In Love

Words & Music by George David Weiss, Hugo Peretti & Luigi Creatore

a tempo ♩ = 90

1. Wise men say, on-ly
(Verses 2,3 & 4 see block lyric)

fools rush in, but

23

24

**D.S. al Coda**

**Coda**

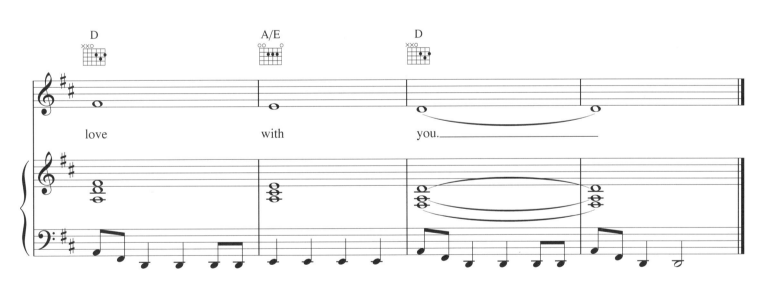

*Verse 2:*
Shall I stay,
Would it be a sin?
If I can't help
Falling in love with you.

*to middle*

*Verse 3:*
Take my hand,
Take my whole life too.
For I can't help
Falling in love with you.

*to middle*

*Verse 4:*
Take my hand,
Take my whole life too.
For I can't help
Falling in love with you.

*to Coda*

# Can't Take My Eyes Off You

Words & Music by Bob Crewe & Bob Gaudio

29

D.%. al Coda

Coda

30

Verse 3:
You're just too good to be true
Can't take my eyes off you
You'd be like heaven to touch
I wanna hold you so much
At long last love has arrived
And I thank God I'm alive
You're just too good to be true
Can't take my eyes off you.

I love you baby *etc.*

31

# (They Long To Be) Close To You

Words by Hal David
Music by Burt Bacharach

they long to be close to you. _____ Why do
stars fall down from the sky ev-'ry time you walk by?__
Just like me __ they long to be

close to you. _____

On the day that you were born the an - gels got to - ge - ther_ And de - ci - ded to cre - ate a dream come true, So they sprink - led moon - dust in your hair_ Of

# Don't Let The Sun Catch You Crying

Words & Music by Gerard Marsden, Fred Marsden, Les Chadwick & Les Maguire

Original key: D♭ major

♩ = 102

1. Don't let the sun catch you cry - in'.

The night's the time for all your tears.

37

38

# The First Cut Is The Deepest

Words & Music by Cat Stevens

**Slowly, with a beat**

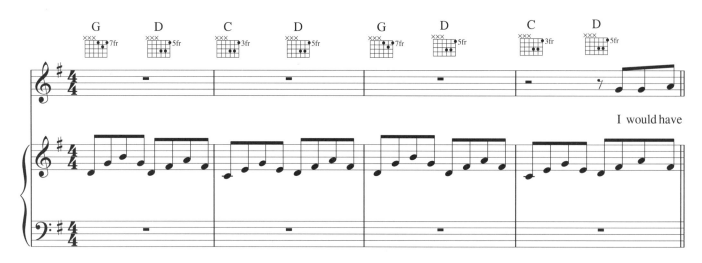

I would have

gi-ven you all__ of my heart,__ but there's some-one who's torn it a-part.__ And she's ta-
want you by__ my side__ just to help me dry the tears that I've cried.__ And I'm

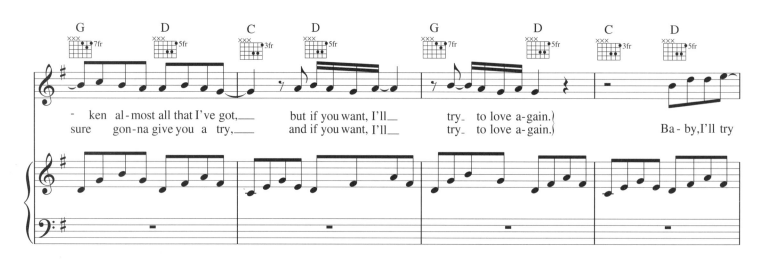

- ken al-most all that I've got,__ but if you want, I'll__ try_ to love a-gain.)
sure gon-na give you a try,__ and if you want, I'll__ try_ to love a-gain.)

Ba-by, I'll try

41

# Fly Me To The Moon (In Other Words)

Words & Music by Bart Howard

**Slowly and tenderly**

45

# Go Now

Words & Music by Larry Banks & Milton Bennett

just what you in-tend to do now._____ Cos

how ma-ny times have to tell you, darl - in', darl - in', darl - in', darl - in', darl -

- in', I'm still in love, still in love__ with

**1.**

you now.   2. We've al - rea - dy said_____

Verse 2:
We've already said, so long
I don't want to see you go
But boy you had better
Go now, go now
Go now, go now
Don't you even try

Bridge 2:
To tell me that you really don't
Want to see it in this way now.
Don't you know
If you really meant what you said
Darlin', darlin', darlin'
I wouldn't have to keep on begging you
Begging you, begging you
Begging you to stay.

Go now *etc.*

# God Only Knows

Words & Music by Brian Wilson & Tony Asher

I'll make you so____ sure a - bout it. God on - ly knows____

*To Coda* ⊕

**1.**

____ what I'd be with - out____ you.

**2.**

N.C. N.C.

Ah,_____ ah._____ Do do do do do do

51

*Verses 2 & 3*
If you should ever leave me,
Though life would still go on, believe me,
The world could show nothing to me,
So what good would living do me?
God only knows what I'd be without you.

# Crazy

Words & Music by Willie Nelson

love me as long as you want-ed,_____ and then some-day_____ you'd leave me for some-bod-y new.

Wor - ry,_____ why do I let my-self wor - ry;_____ Won-d'rin'_____

what in the world did I do.

Cra - zy _____ for think - ing that my love could hold you,_____

I'm cra - zy for try - in', cra - zy for cry - in'_____ and I'm

**1**
cra - zy for lov - in' you.

**2**
you.

# Here, There And Everywhere

Words & Music by John Lennon & Paul McCartney

# I Can't Stop Loving You

Words & Music by Don Gibson

It's use-less to say,_____ so I'll just live my life_____

in dreams of yes - ter - days._____ Those__ hap - py

hours that we__once knew, though__ long a-go__

_____ they still__ make me blue._____ They say__ that

time heals a bro-ken heart,___ but time has stood

still,_____ since we've been a - part._____ (I can't stop

lov - ing you), I've made up my mind,_____

to live in me - mo-ries_____ of the lone - some time.

(I can't stop want - ing you).                    It's use-less to

say,_____    so I'll just live my life_____

in dreams of yes - ter - days._____             (Those hap - py

hours              that we__ once  knew,     though long  a -

# I Close My Eyes And Count To Ten

Words & Music by Clive Westlake

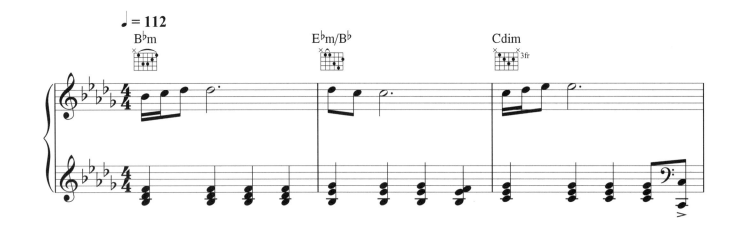

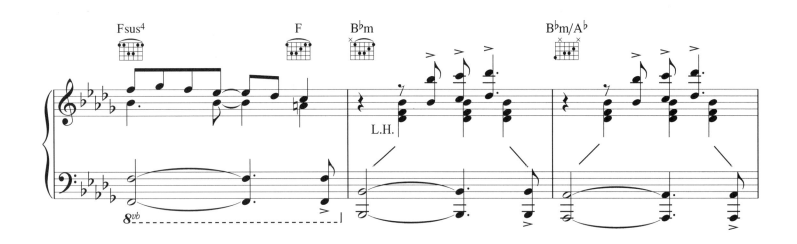

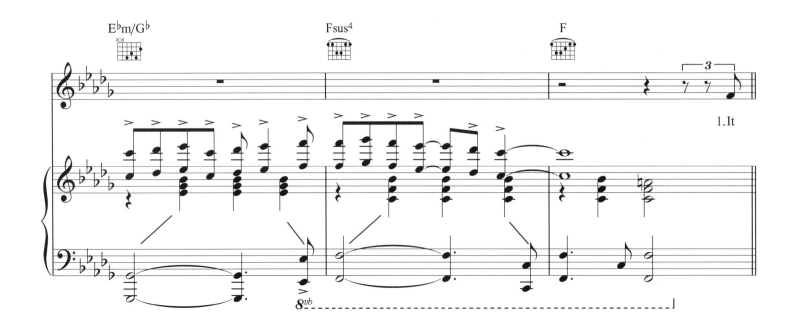

isn't the way that you look, and it isn't the way that you

talk. It isn't the things that you say or do make me

want you so.___ It is nothing to do___ with the
(2.) strangers a moment a-

wine or the music that's flooding my___ mind. Oh,
-go with a few dreams but nothing to___ show. The

# I Say A Little Prayer

Words by Hal David.  Music by Burt Bacharach

74

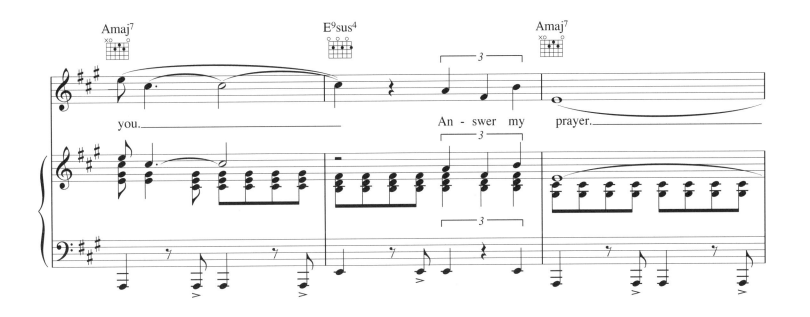

you._____  An - swer my   prayer._____

Say  you  love  me  too._____

*dim. poco a poco*

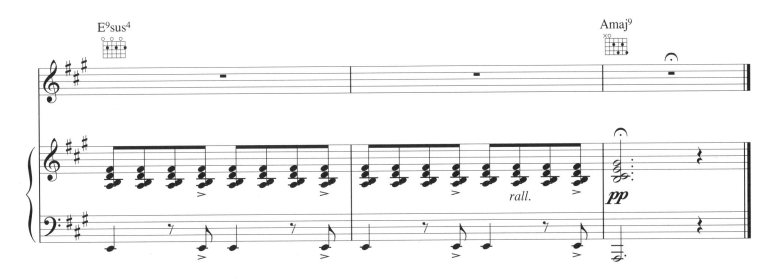

*rall.*

*pp*

*Verse 2:*
I run for the bus, dear.
While riding, I think of us dear.
I say a little prayer for you.
At work I just take time,
And all through my coffee break time
I say a little prayer for you.

# I Left My Heart In San Francisco

Words by Douglas Cross
Music by George Cory

climb half-way to the stars, _____ the morn-ing

fog _____ may chill the air, I don't

care! My love was there in San Fran-

cis-co, _____ a-bove the blue _____

79

# The Minute You're Gone

Words & Music by Jimmy Gateley

The min - ute you're gone_____ I cry,

the min - ute you're gone_____ I die.

Be - fore you____ walk out_____ of sight

81

the min - ute you're_ gone.

The min - ute you're_ gone_____ I see

how lone - ly a man__ I'd__ be. My life would_ be

oh,__ so blue_____ if I____ could-n't be____ with you._____

# (Take A Little) Piece Of My Heart

Words & Music by Jerry Ragovoy & Bert Berns

Break it, break a-no-ther lit-tle bit of my heart____ now ho-ney.

Have a, have a-no-ther lit-tle piece of my heart____ now ba-by.

1.

2.

*D. %: to fade*

You know you've got it if it makes you feel good. 2. You're makes you feel good. Hey ____

*Verse 2:*
You're out on the street (looking good)
And you know deep down in your heart that ain't right
And oh, you never hear me when I cry at night
I tell myself that I can't stand the pain
But when you hold me in your arms I say it again.

So come on *etc.*

# Somethin' Stupid

Words & Music by C. Carson Parks

know I stand in line un - til you think you have the time to spend an

F♯m7 B7 F♯m7 B7 F♯m7 B7 F♯m7
ev-'ning with me, and if we go some place to dance I
B7 F♯m7 B7 E E6
know that there's a chance you won't be leav - ing with me.
Emaj7 E6 E7 Bm7 E7 Bm7
Then af - ter-wards we drop in - to a qui - et lit - tle place and have a
A C7 F♯m7 B7
drink or two, and then I go and spoil it all by

89

prac - tise ev - 'ry day to find some cle - ver lines___ to say to make the
*(2° Instrumental until *)*

mean - ing come true,___ but

then I think I'll wait un - til the ev - 'ning gets late and I'm

-lone with you.___ * The time is right, your per - fume fills my

91

# This Guy's In Love With You

Words by Hal David
Music by Burt Bacharach

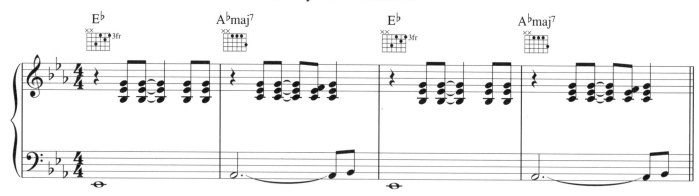

You see___ this guy,___ this guy's in love with you.___

___ Yes, I'm___ in love.___ Who

looks at you the way I do?___ When you smile,__

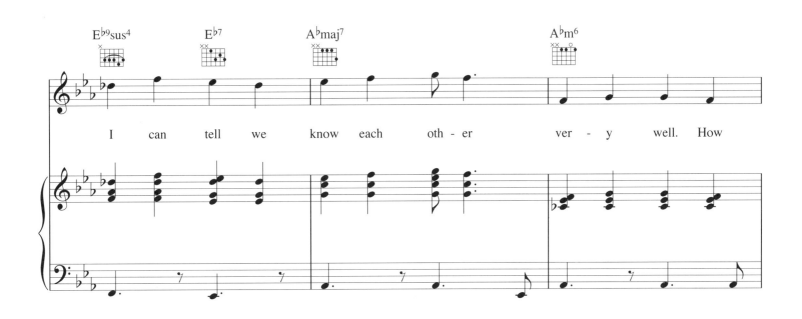

I can tell we know each oth-er ver-y well. How

can I show you I'm glad I

got    to    know you? 'Cause    I've heard__ some talk._____    They

*2nd time fade out within ten measures*

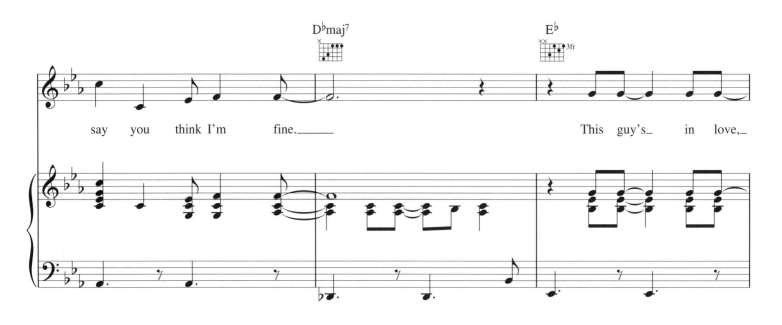

say    you    think I'm    fine._____    This guy's__    in love,__

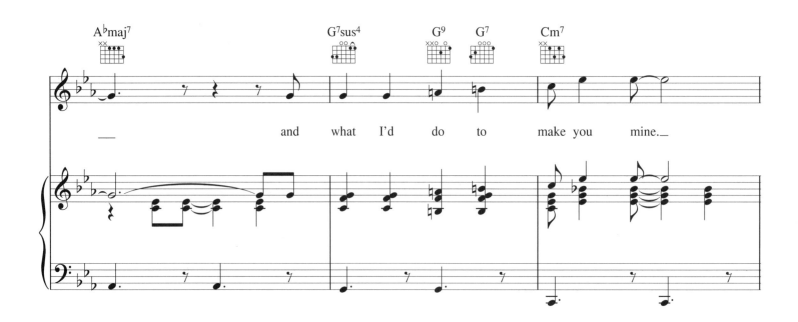

and    what    I'd    do    to    make you    mine.__

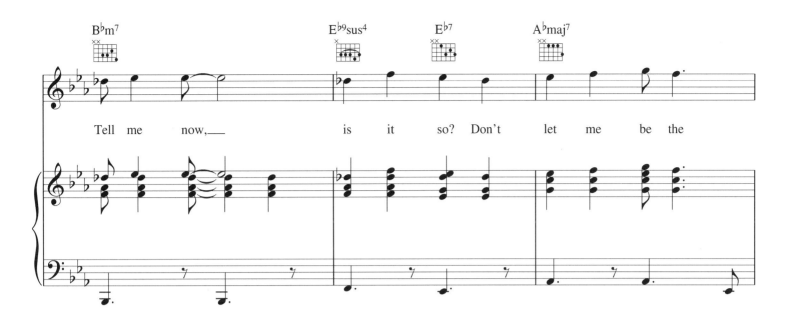

Tell me now,___ is it so? Don't let me be the

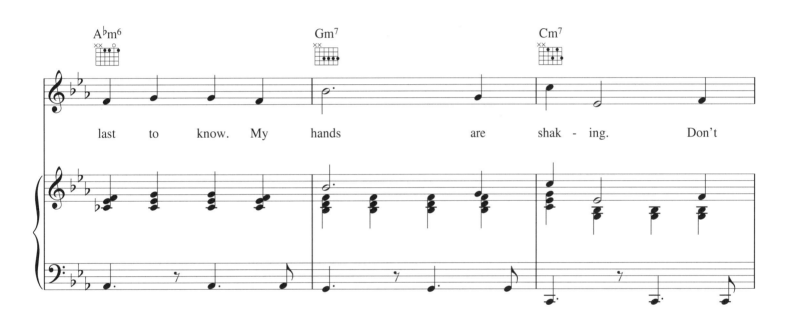

last to know. My hands are shak - ing. Don't

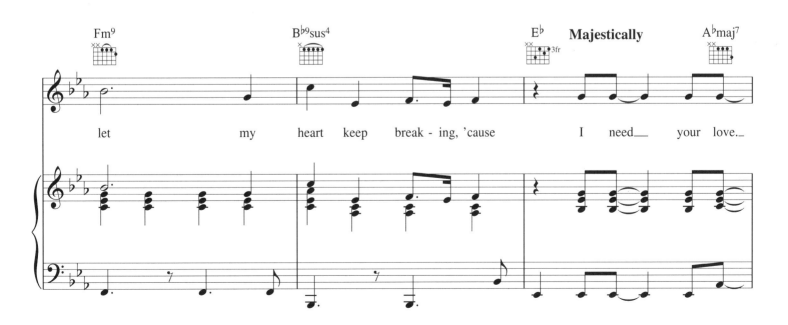

let my heart keep break - ing, 'cause I need___ your love.___

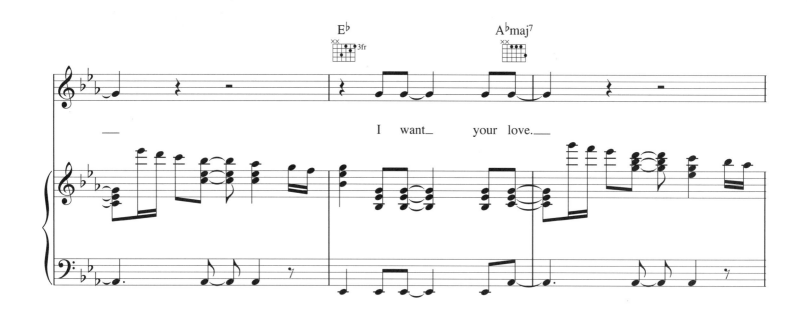
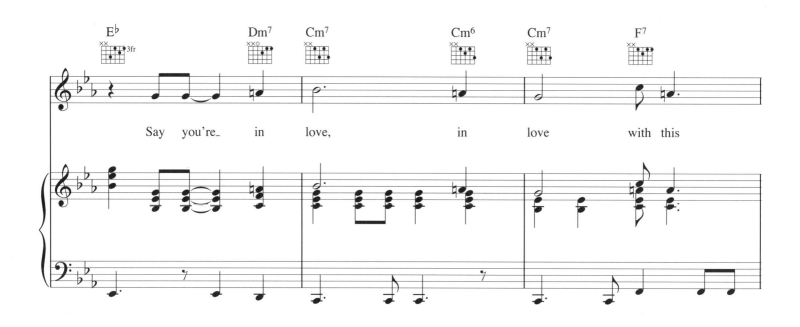
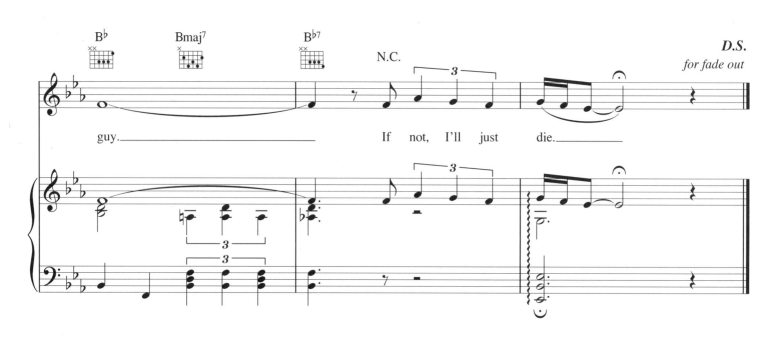

# Until It's Time For You To Go

Words & Music by Buffy Sainte-Marie

A♭ (A)
A♭maj7/G (Amaj7/G♯)
G♭ (G)
space in the lives that we'd planned.
stayed out-side my heart but in you came.
F (F♯)
B♭m (Bm)
E♭ (E)
And here we'll stay un - til it's time for you to
And here you'll stay un - til it's time for you to
1. A♭ (A)
E♭/G (E/G♯)
2. A♭ (A)
go. 2.Yes, we're go.
A (B♭)
G♭* (G*)
A♭* (A*)
3fr
5fr
Don't ask why.

# Unchained Melody

Words by Hy Zaret
Music by Alex North

mine? _____ I need your love, _____ I need your love, _____

— God speed your love _____ to me! _____

1. Lone - ly riv - ers flow \_\_\_\_\_ to the sea, \_\_\_\_\_ to the sea,
2. Lone - ly moun - tains gaze \_\_\_\_\_ at the stars, \_\_\_\_\_ at the stars,

To the o - pen arms \_\_\_\_\_ of the sea. \_\_\_\_\_
Wait - ing for the dawn \_\_\_\_\_ of the day. \_\_\_\_\_

# Words

Words & Music by Barry Gibb, Maurice Gibb & Robin Gibb

1. Smile, an ev-er-last-ing smile, a smile can bring you near to me.
*(Verses 2 & 3 see block lyric)*

Don't ev - er let me find you gone cos that would bring a tear___ to me.

2° Tacet

This world has lost its glo - ry, let's start a brand___ new sto - ry

now, my love. You think that I don't ev - en

mean a sin - gle word I say. It's on - ly

words,     and words are all I have     to take your heart a - way.

**1.**

**2, 3.**

It's on - ly     words,     and words are all I

have     to take your heart a - way.

It's on - ly____

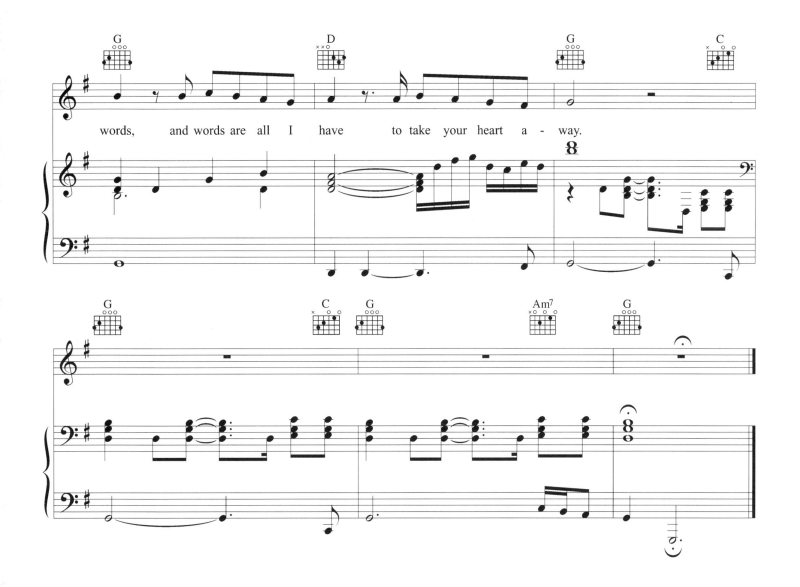

words,    and words are all I have    to take your heart a - way.

*Verse 2:*
Talk in everlasting words
And dedicate them all to me
And I will give you all my life
I'm here if you should call to me
You think that I don't even mean
A single word I say.

It's only words *etc.*

*Verse 3:*
Da da da da... *(8 bars)*

This world has lost its glory
Let's start a brand new story now, my love
You think that I don't even mean
A single word I say.

It's only words *etc.*

123456789

# Bringing you the words and the music

All the latest music in print... rock & pop plus jazz, blues, country, classical and the best in West End show scores.

- Books to match your favourite CDs.

- Book-and-CD titles with high quality backing tracks for you to play along to. Now you can play guitar or piano with your favourite artist... or simply sing along!

- Audition songbooks with CD backing tracks for both male and female singers for all those with stars in their eyes.

- Can't read music? No problem, you can still play all the hits with our wide range of chord songbooks.

- Check out our range of instrumental tutorial titles, taking you from novice to expert in no time at all!

- Musical show scores include *The Phantom Of The Opera*, *Les Misérables*, *Mamma Mia* and many more hit productions.

- DVD master classes featuring the techniques of top artists.